~ Dedicated to my beautiful children,
Eli and Millie.
Most certainly my inspiration.
Without doubt my world ~

This book belongs to:

This is me!

Draw a picture of yourself here!

Eli would love to see your pictures, share your picture and tag us on Instagram using #elisstorywmmm

Published in the United Kingdom by:
Alphabet Moon Publishing Ltd

E-mail: info@elisstory.com

Written by Tracey Lear

Illustrated by Matea Anić
www.mateaanic.com

ISBN: 978-1-7392447-1-2

Eli's story

What makes me, ME!

When Eli was a young boy he thought
the world should see,
inside his world of autism and how
interesting it could be.

`I think I'll write a story,' he said,
`...maybe some poetry.
To help explain my autism and how
autism makes me, me!'

The moon lit up the room that night
as Eli made his plan
to tell his friends about autism
and help them understand.

The next day, he gathered his
friends around and
asked them all to listen.

While he read aloud
`What makes me, ME!',
the story of his autism.

`I know that I am different,
but I also know I'm bright.
Yes, there's things that challenge me.
Just give me time, I'll get it right.'

'I see the world quite differently,
but that doesn't make it wrong.
The world would be so boring,
if we all sang the same song.'

`Autism makes me who I am,
it's a special part of me.
I'd love for you to see
the world through my eyes,
and what I see.'

`My
feelings
can confuse
me, but I feel them,
same as you. I just need
time to work them out.
Things make more sense when I do.'

WHICH EMOTIONS CAN YOU SEE?

`I love my friends and love to play,
I love doing the things you do.

But when I find things tricky,
some funny feelings loom.

`My smile disappears and my
emotions overwhelm me.

So I'll sit back,
take some deep breaths
and count to 10,
this helps me!'

'I'm in a world of my own a lot,
I like having my own space.

It's not that I am being rude,
it's just my happier place.'

`My little sister Millie is
too young to understand.
But she's the one I don't mind
so much, when she wants to
hold my hand.'

`Some things that you find easy,
like conversations about your day.
I find quite hard, so may not answer
questions straight away.

`Autism affects my senses,
like sight, smell, sound and touch.
I may even cover my ears
sometimes when noises get too much.'

HA!
HA!
HA!
BANG
BANG
BANG

'Some say I have a super power
but that isn't completely true,
we all have our own super powers you
see, you just need to look inside you.'

'So let's all embrace our differences.
Have a think, what makes you, you?
And once you know them, own them!
It's what we all should do.'

`Our differences are beautiful.
It's these that light a room.
I'm autistic and I'm proud of it.
Be strong, be proud, be you!

`Coz everyone is different,
that so much is true.
It's the differences in all of us
that really makes you, YOU!'

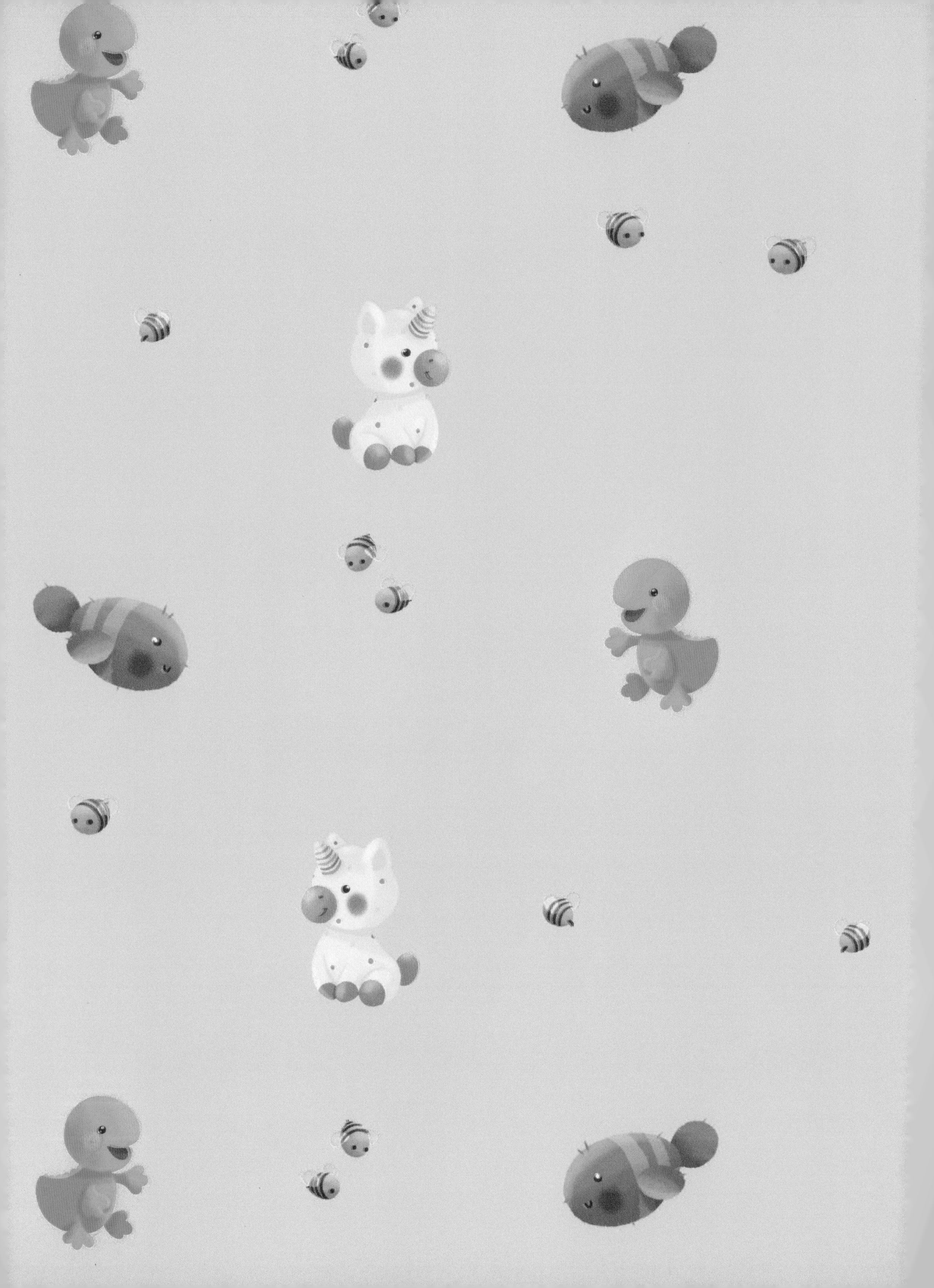

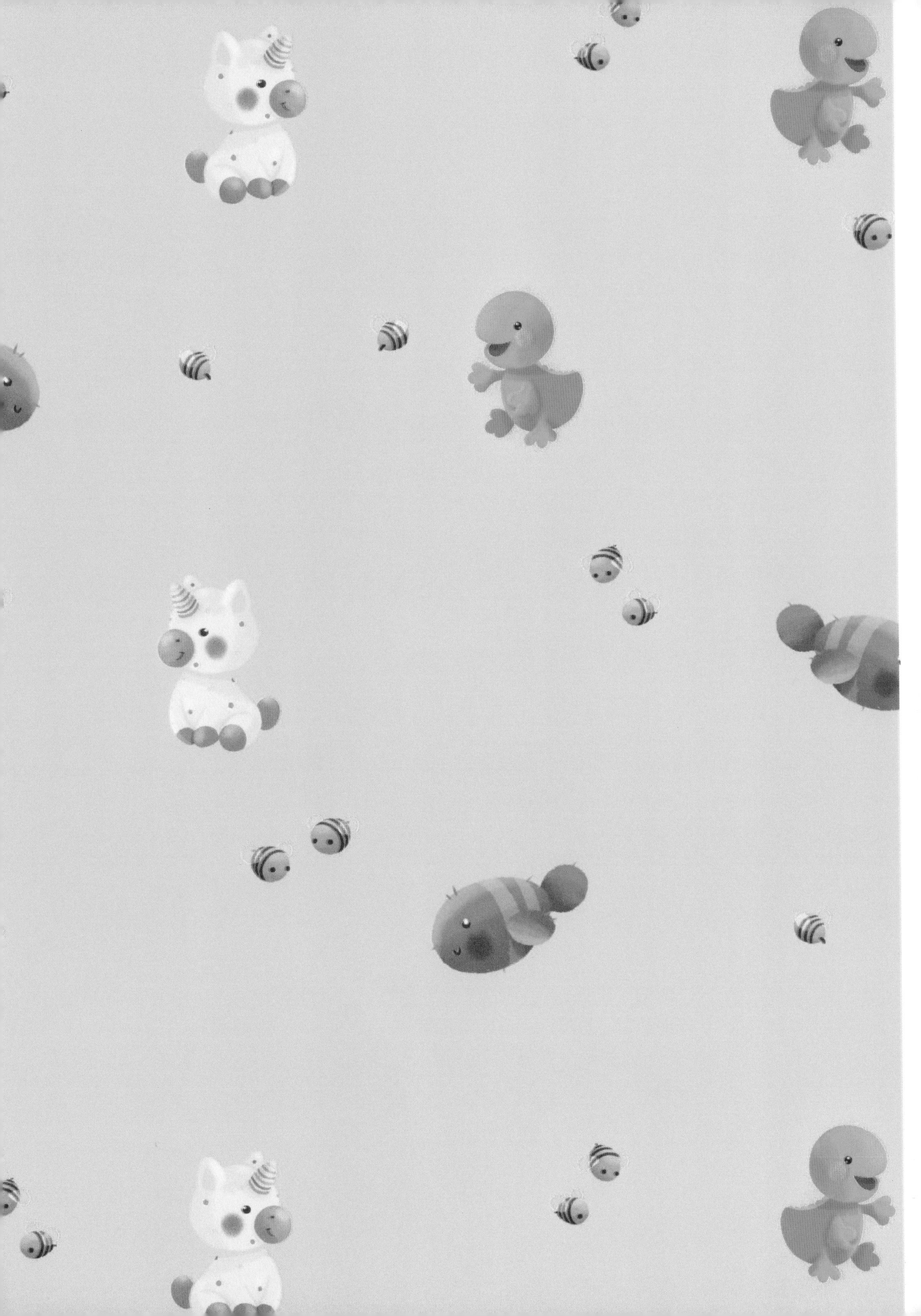

ELI'S STORY

Our book was written to encourage other children and Mummy's and Daddy's to start talking more about autism and help other's feel brave enough to tell their stories too.

Everyone should talk about what makes them different. If I wasn't autistic, I wouldn't be me.

FUN FACTS ABOUT ME:

I really love planets

Diagnosed autistic at 4 yrs old

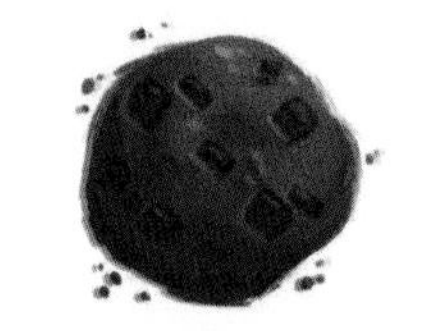

Fave food chicken nuggets & cookies

Eli's story came from a poem my mummy wrote for me to read to my class

'the world would be so boring if we all sang the same song'

Printed in Great Britain
by Amazon